Contents

Andrew Brodie: Festivals Across the Year 5-7 © A C Black Publishers Ltd. 2007

Introduction

This book features information and activity sheets on fourteen significant festivals throughout the year. It is designed to familiarise primary-aged children with some of the celebrations and customs of the world's major religions and cultures.

The festivals are arranged in approximate chronological order, starting from September and working around the school year. Note, however, that some festivals change date each year – the Christian festival of Easter and the Islamic festival of Eid ul-Fitr, for example. Further guidance about the order in which the festivals occur can be found on Resource Sheets C and D (page 61-62).

For each festival there are four pages, the first of which provides comprehensive background information for teachers, followed by three worksheets. The worksheets are intended primarily for use in RE lessons but many could also be used in assemblies or in after school clubs. The sheets can be photocopied on to OHP transparencies for group work. The worksheets should give children an understanding of the story behind each religious or cultural festival, and some of the main traditions and customs involved.

At the end of the book there are six Resource Sheets for teachers. These sheets can be used to consolidate or expand the children's knowledge of the religions included in this book. These Resource Sheets include the following:

Resource Sheet A An overview of the cycle of festivals each year.

Resource Sheet B An overview of the cycle of festivals each year.

Resource Sheet C Religious symbols: Sikhism, Islam, Hinduism

Resource Sheet D Religious symbols: Buddhism, Christianity, Judaism

Resource Sheet E A simple frame with writing lines to enable pictures and writing about any festival. This can be used for pupils to provide writing and a picture or for the adult to provide the writing for a child to illustrate.

Resource Sheet F A festivals word puzzle. This simple puzzle provides a consolidation and revision activity.

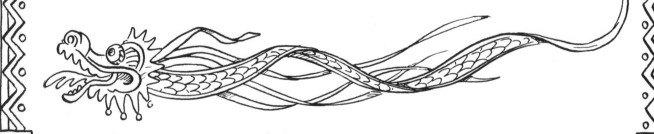

Harvest

Teacher's Notes

Background information

Harvest celebrations in Great Britain date back to long before the advent of Christianity. For as long as people have grown crops to eat, their survival has depended on the success of the harvest. Harvest Festivals are believed to have become part of the Christian calendar in 1843 when a church in Cornwall held a special harvest thanksgiving service in the autumn of that year.

Christian churches now hold services with Harvest hymns and prayers each autumn, and are decorated with seasonal fruit and vegetables. This harvest produce is often distributed to the elderly or those in need when the celebrations are over.

Now that so much of our food comes pre-washed, pre-chopped and pre-packaged from supermarkets, many children are so far removed from farming and food in its natural state that it is easy to forget the importance of a good harvest. Harvest Festival provides a good opportunity to think about where foods come from and how and where they are grown. It can also provide an opportunity to discuss the contrast in food distribution between rich and poor countries, helping those in need, and being thankful for what we have.

Practical activities

Provide a variety of freshly grown produce for the children to look at and taste. Explain to pupils that not all items purchased from supermarkets are grown locally, and that many have had to be shipped thousands of miles from all around the world. Encourage pupils to recognise which items are fruit and which are vegetables, and learn that fruit and vegetables are very important components in a healthy diet. Teach them that bread is made from wheat grown in the fields, and how a good or bad harvest affects all the food we eat.

Give the pupils simple pictures of plates on which to draw their favourite meals, and ask them to include both fruit and vegetable items. Alternatively, buy large and small paper plates for every member of the class on which to draw their healthy main course and healthy dessert.

Worksheet 1 is a Harvest poem with missing words for the children to fill in. You could use this poem as a guided reading activity or in an assembly. It is also suitable for Harvest performances.

Worksheet 2 is a picture of a supermarket-style counter of fruit and vegetables. The children should write names of the appropriate food on the labels.

Worksheet 3 provides a gift tag for the children to decorate and attach to a Harvest basket for someone they know.

Andrew Brodie: Festivals Across the Year 5-7 © A C Black Publishers Ltd. 2007

Harvest

Name .... Date ....

Read the poem. Choose the missing words from the basket and put them into the poem.

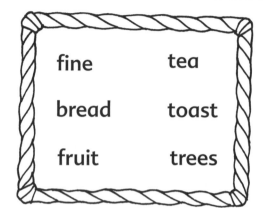

fine   tea

bread   toast

fruit   trees

I like to eat tomatoes red,

And butter spread on crusty _____ .

Potatoes mashed, or boiled, or roast.

Strawberry jam upon some _____ .

Onions, marrows, cooked beetroot.

Cherries and grapes are tasty _____ .

Gently swaying in the breeze

Are apples and pears hanging from the _____ .

These foods that grow are good for me

To eat at breakfast, lunch and _____ .

We thank the Lord at Harvest time

For giving us these foods so _____ .

Andrew Brodie: Festivals Across the Year 5-7 © A C Black Publishers Ltd. 2007

Harvest

Name ....

Date ....

Label the fruit and vegetables you can see in the picture.
Carefully colour the picture when you have finished.

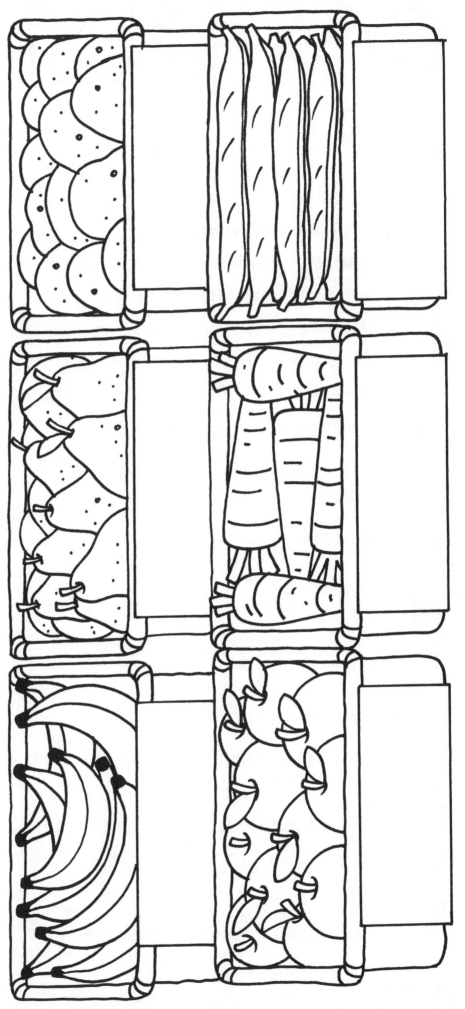

Harvest

Name .... Date ....

Put a Harvest basket together for someone you know. You could fill it with all sorts of food. Then cut out the tag below. Decorate it and write a Harvest message on it. Cut out the dotted circle and attach the tag to your basket with a piece of string or ribbon before you give it away.

Andrew Brodie: Festivals Across the Year 5–7 © A C Black Publishers Ltd. 2007

Eid ul-Fitr

Teacher's Notes

Background information

The Islamic faith is based on five ideals and beliefs called the Five Pillars of Islam. These are:

Shahadah – The Muslim profession of faith that there is only one God and Muhammad was His final prophet
Salah – Performing ritual prayers five times a day
Zakah – Giving a portion of one's wealth each year for charitable causes
Sawm – Fasting during the month of Ramadan
Hajj – Making a pilgrimage to the holy Ka'bah at Mecca.

Eid ul-Fitr is the festival which celebrates the end of the month of Ramadan, when Muslims fast every day from dawn until dusk. The fasting helps Muslims to remember when the prophet Muhammad was given the sacred texts which form the Qur'an, the holy book of Islam. It encourages self-discipline and also helps Muslims to understand the sufferings of the poor and hungry, and to have sympathy for them. During Ramadan there is a focus on prayer, reading and learning the Qur'an, forgiveness and charity. Muslims are discouraged from partaking in worldly pursuits such as idle chatter or watching television, and are expected to avoid any kind of evil thoughts or actions. Each day, after the sun

has set, many people attend the mosque to eat together. Some people are excused from fasting at Ramadan, including those who are sick or very old, children under the age of twelve, and those travelling on long journeys.

At the end of Ramadan, houses are decorated with garlands and lights for Eid ul-Fitr to celebrate the end of fasting. Muslims get up very early and go to the mosque, wearing their best clothes, to thank Allah for the self-discipline he has given them during the month of Ramadan. After praying at the mosque, gifts and cards are exchanged at parties and family feasts. Muslims also give money to the poor at Eid ul-Fitr, so that they are also able to enjoy the festival. People say 'Eid Mubarak' to each other, which means 'Happy Festival'. Eid ul-Fitr is all about coming together, and renewing friendships and family ties.

The Islamic calendar is based on lunar months, so Eid ul-Fitr is celebrated when the new moon is seen, signifying the start of the month called Shawwal. This means that the date of the festival varies throughout the western year as the lunar calendar can be around 11 days shorter. Eid takes place around 13th October 2007, 2nd October 2008, 21st September 2009 and 10th September 2010.

Worksheet 1 is a matching activity about the customs of Eid ul-Fitr. This is suitable for children to write or stick the sentences in the correct places.

Worksheet 2 provides a template for an Eid fanoo lantern to decorate the classroom.

Worksheet 3 is a design for a greetings card to be coloured and completed.

Andrew Brodie: Festivals Across the Year 5–7 © A C Black Publishers Ltd. 2007

Eid ul-Fitr

Name .... Date ....

Match the pictures to the sentences. Write each sentence below the correct picture.

_____

_____

_____

_____

_____

_____

| At Eid ul-Fitr people dress in new clothes. | They visit the Mosque to pray together. |
| Presents and cards are given to friends and family. | Families enjoy large feasts together. |

Andrew Brodie: Festivals Across the Year 5-7 © A C Black Publishers Ltd. 2007

Eid ul-Fitr

Name ....

Date ....

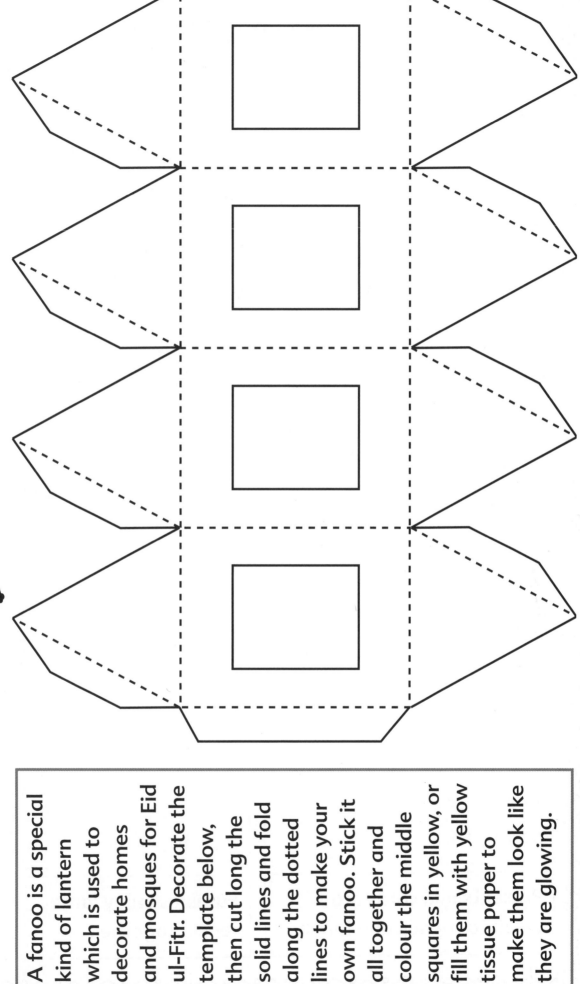

A fanoo is a special kind of lantern which is used to decorate homes and mosques for Eid ul-Fitr. Decorate the template below, then cut long the solid lines and fold along the dotted lines to make your own fanoo. Stick it all together and colour the middle squares in yellow, or fill them with yellow tissue paper to make them look like they are glowing.

Andrew Brodie: Festivals Across the Year 5–7 © A C Black Publishers Ltd. 2007

10

Eid ul-Fitr

Name ....

Date ....

At the festival of Eid ul-Fitr people give one another cards.

The greeting 'Eid Mubarak' means Happy Festival. Cut out and colour this card.

Yom Kippur and Sukkot

Teacher's Notes

Background information

Sukkot is one of the three major Jewish festivals, known as the three pilgrim festivals, which celebrate the Exodus of the early Jews (or Israelites) who Moses led from slavery in Egypt. It is a joyful festival in which Jews thank God for his provision and protection in the forty years that they spent wandering in the desert on their way to the Promised Land of Israel. Sukkot is traditionally a harvest festival, and a chance to thank God for what he has provided throughout the year.

Sukkot is also known as the 'festival of booths' as Jews mark the festival by building small huts made from natural materials, similar to those that the Israelites made for shelter in the desert. The Torah (the Jewish holy book) gives instructions that after the fields have been harvested there should be seven days of celebration, and that 'all the people of Israel shall live in shelters for seven days, so that your descendents may know that the Lord made the people of Israel live in simple shelters when he led them out of Egypt' (Leviticus 23: 42). This kind of hut or shelter is called a 'sukkah', and has at least three sides and a roof which is partly open to the sky. It is decorated with fruit and vegetables hanging from the ceiling. Whilst nowadays not everyone chooses to build and live in the sukkah for seven days, particularly those in colder countries, they will however often eat meals in the sukkah and are supposed to treat it as their home.

Another important ritual which takes place on each day of Sukkot is the ritual waving of the Four Species. The Torah commands Jews to take branches from four plants: the lulav (date palm), hadass (myrtle tree), aravah (willow) and etrog (citron). The waving of these plants usually takes place in the synagogue, and the branches are waved to all four sides, as well as upwards and downwards, while this blessing is recited: 'Blessed are You, God our Lord, King of the Universe, Who has sanctified us with His commandments and commanded us to take the lulav'. These plants are often also used to build the sukkah.

Sukkot usually takes place in the last half of September or the first part of October, coming just four days after Yom Kippur. It starts on 27th September 2007, 14th October 2008, 3rd October 2009 and 23rd September 2010.

Worksheet 1 is a missing word activity providing general information about Sukkot.

Worksheet 2 asks the children to draw a sukkah to a simple design brief.

Worksheet 3 is a fun Sukkot picture maze activity.

Andrew Brodie: Festivals Across the Year 5–7 © A C Black Publishers Ltd 2007

Yom Kippur and Sukkot

Name .... Date ....

Read each sentence about Sukkot. Find the missing word at the bottom of the page and write it in the space.

● Sukkot is the name of a harvest festival celebrated by

_____ all over the world.

● A sukkah is a _____ which Jews must build

and live in for the seven days of Sukkot.

● The Israelites used to build a sukkah for shelter when

they travelled through the _____ .

● The Israelites travelled for _____ years to

escape from being slaves in Egypt.

● At Sukkot, Jews wave branches from four different

plants called the Four _____.

● These four plants are often used to build the _____.

● Sukkot is also a time to thank God for a good _____.

| Species | Jews | forty | sukkah | harvest | hut | desert |

Andrew Brodie: Festivals Across the Year 5-7 © A C Black Publishers Ltd. 2007

Name .... Date ....

Yom Kippur and Sukkot

Draw a sukkah that you and your family could stay in during Sukkot.

Remember that:

It must have at least three sides.

There should be a space in the roof so that you can see the sky.

The roof should be made from natural materials like wood and branches.

Sukkot is a harvest festival and your sukkah should be decorated with fruits and vegetables.

14

Name ....

Date ....

Yom Kippur and Sukkot

Match each person to the correct hut.

Colour the picture.

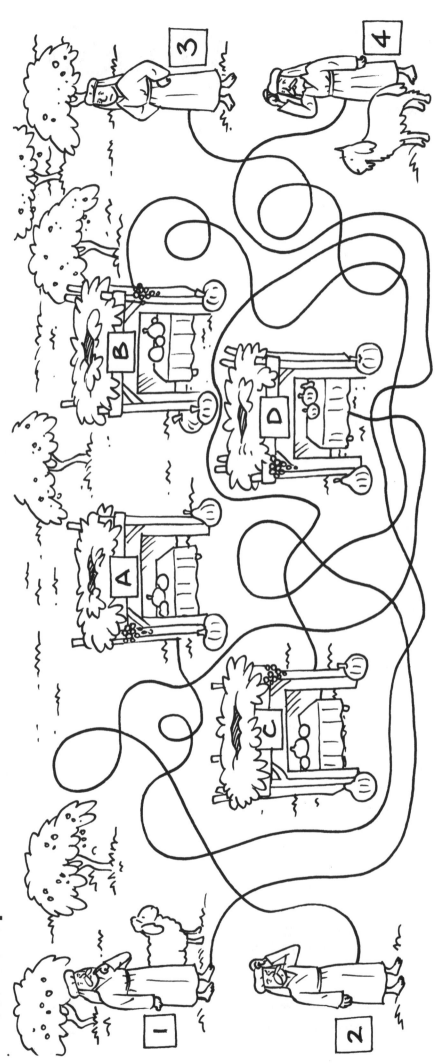

Diwali

Teacher's Notes

Background information

Diwali (sometimes spelt Divali) is known as the 'festival of lights' and is the most important festival in the Hindu calendar. It celebrates the victory of good over evil and of light over darkness.

Hindus celebrate Diwali for many reasons, but the most common story behind the festival is that of how Rama rescued his wife, Sita, from Ravana, the ten headed demon.

The goddess of wealth, Lakshmi, is also honoured at Diwali. Some Hindus build a shrine to Lakshmi and decorate it with money to thank her for the rewards of wealth they have received. They leave their doors and windows open so that she can enter their houses, and use oil lamps called divas to light the way for her. Brightly coloured symmetrical patterns called rangoli are made on doorsteps from rice to welcome Lakshmi.

Diwali is a joyful festival characterised by decorative lights and diva lamps. People visit relatives, and exchange gifts and cards. There are feasts, parties, joyful festivities and bright firework displays.

Whilst Diwali is thought of mainly as a Hindu festival, it is also celebrated by Sikhs. At Diwali,

Sikhs remember when Guru Hargobind, the sixth guru, was released from imprisonment by the Mughal emperor. They also celebrate the laying of the first stone of the Golden Temple at Amritsar, the holiest place in the Sikh world, which took place at Diwali.

Diwali is held in late October or early November. It takes place on 9th November 2007, 28th October 2008, 17th October 2009 and 5th November 2010.

Worksheet 1 is a basic cloze procedure text about Diwali and its customs. This could be used as a classroom or assembly activity. The text could be photocopied on to acetate and the words cut out so they can be placed in the correct places during the assembly.

Worksheet 2 tells the story of Rama and Sita with spaces for children to draw their own pictures.

Worksheet 3 gives some incomplete rangoli patterns that the children must complete using symmetry.

Andrew Brodie: Festivals Across the Year 5–7 © A C Black Publishers Ltd 2007

15

Diwali

Name .... Date ....

Use words from the lamp to complete the writing.

happy
lights
homes
parties
presents
patterns
November

Diwali is celebrated each year in October or _____ .

It is a very _____ time when people enjoy dancing,

singing and going to_____ . Families and friends

may give each other _____ and cards. At Diwali

people decorate their _____ with lamps and _____ ,

and even enjoy bright firework displays.

Special patterns called rangoli _____ are drawn and

brightly coloured.

Andrew Brodie: Festivals Across the Year 5-7 © A C Black Publishers Ltd. 2007

Diwali

Name .... Date ....

Draw pictures in the boxes to go with the story.

1. Prince Rama and his wife Sita were sent away by the king.

2. Rama and Sita went to live in the forest. They were very happy there and made friends with the forest creatures.

3. Ravana, an evil ten-headed demon, caught Sita and took her to his island prison.

4. The monkey army helped Rama to rescue Sita and take her safely home.

Diwali

Name .... Date ....

At Diwali, Hindus make brightly coloured symmetrical patterns outside their front doors to welcome in the goddess Lakshmi. These patterns are called Rangoli. Finish the patterns and colour them brightly. The colouring should be symmetrical too.

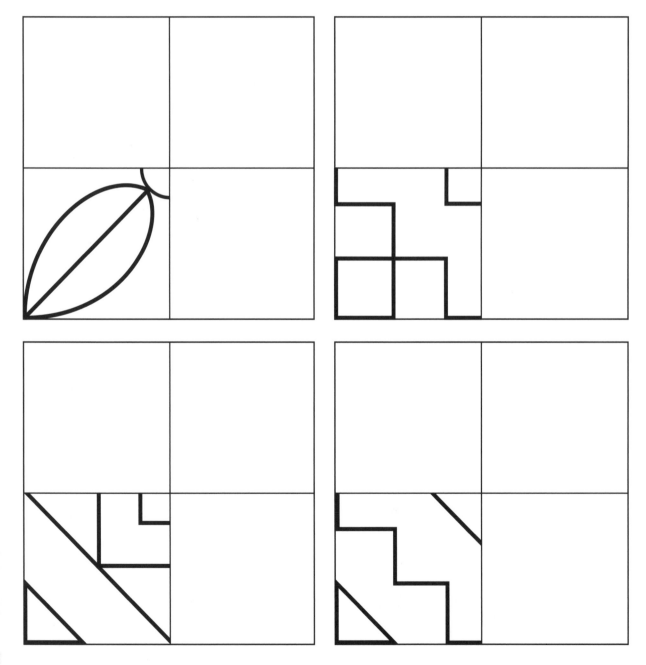

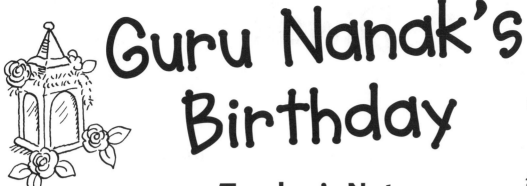

Guru Nanak's Birthday

Teacher's Notes

Background information

Guru Nanak was the first of the ten Sikh Gurus, or teachers of the Sikh faith. Sikhs commemorate many aspects of the Gurus' lives, particularly their births and deaths, and they call these occasions 'gurpurbs' (this is sometimes written 'gurpurabs'). Guru Nanak's birthday is the most celebrated gurpurb, and is marked each November or April, depending on whether the lunar or the Nanakshahi calendar is used to fix the date.

Guru Nanak was the founder of the Sikh religion. He was born in 1469 near Lahore and began his teaching when he was about thirty years old. The area in which he lived was divided between Hindus and Muslims at the time.

Sikhs mark each gurpurb by reading the Guru Granth Sahib (the Sikh holy book which is also regarded as the eleventh and final Guru) from beginning to end. This ritual, known as an 'akhand path' takes 48 hours and is done by a team of Sikhs who take it in turns to read sections, ensuring that no gaps or breaks occur in the reading. This usually takes place at gurdwaras (Sikh temples), which are decorated with lights, flowers and flags for the occasion.

Sikhs dress up in their best clothes to go to the gurdwara where they sing hymns from the Guru Granth Sahib and listen to stories and poems about Guru Nanak. In India there are often processions carrying the Guru Granth Sahib through the streets, with singers and martial artists.

Worksheet 1 tells a story about Guru Nanak and asks the children to provide an illustration.

Worksheet 2 is a cloze procedure about Guru Nanak's Birthday.

Worksheet 3 is a word search to reinforce vocabulary related to Sikhism and Guru Nanak's Birthday.

Andrew Brodie: Festivals Across the Year 5–7 © A C Black Publishers Ltd 2007

Guru Nanak's Birthday

Guru Nanak was the man who started Sikhism. Sikhs everywhere celebrate his birthday. Read the story below about Guru Nanak.

When Guru Nanak was a boy he thought a lot about God. One day his father gave him some money to buy goods from the market. He was to buy foods that could be sold by the family to make a profit. Nanak's friend Bala went with him.

On the way to market the two boys passed a group of men praying. They looked very thin and Nanak found out that they had not had anything to eat for days.

At the market Nanak and Bala spent the money that Nanak's father had given them. They bought juicy fresh fruits and crisp ripe vegetables. On their way home they again met the holy men. To Bala's surprise, Nanak gave all of the food to the hungry men and returned home with nothing.

Nanak's father was very angry and demanded to know why Nanak hadn't gone home with a good bargain. He was most surprised when Nanak calmly told him that he had got an excellent bargain. 'What better bargain could there be than feeding the poor?' he said.

That story shows how Nanak was concerned with helping others from a very early age .

Now draw a picture to go with the story on a separate sheet of paper.

Guru Nanak's Birthday

Name .... Date ....

Put the words from the box in the correct spaces.

Gurpurb	everyone
eleventh	Granth
poems	together
birthday	Nanak's
drinks	

A festival for the birthday of a guru is called a 'Gurpurb'. Guru Nanak's birthday is the most popular

_____ . Guru is a word meaning teacher. Guru

Nanak was the first of ten human gurus. The _____

guru is a book of songs and _____ written by some of

the gurus. The book has a special name: it is called 'Guru Granth

Sahib'.

On all the gurpurbs the Guru _____ Sahib (the special

book) is read aloud from beginning to end. On Guru Nanak's

_____ there may be a procession and food and

_____ are given out to people who are watching it.

Guru Nanak told people that _____ was equal.

No one was more important than anyone else. He said that

everybody should sit together to eat. Sikhs all sit

_____ to enjoy a meal when they are celebrating

Guru _____ birthday.

Andrew Brodie: Festivals Across the Year 5–7 © A C Black Publishers Ltd 2007

Guru Nanak's Birthday

Name .... Date ....

Look for the words in the word search. They might be written forwards or backwards, up or down.

Guru Nanak		Gurpurb		flag

	meal		birthday	

G	U	R	U	N	A	N	A	K	G
U	P	A	R	A	D	E	M	D	U
R	Q	R	S	H	G	F	E	C	R
D	B	I	R	T	H	D	A	Y	P
W	P	M	O	I	S	E	L	F	U
A	F	E	S	T	I	V	A	L	R
R	K	L	H	J	K	B	A	A	B
A	T	E	A	C	H	E	R	G	A

gurdwara		Sikh		teacher

	festival		parade	

Hanukkah

Teacher's Notes

Hanukkah is the Jewish Festival of Lights, and is observed by Jews all around the world.

It marks the triumph of a group of Jews, known as the Maccabees, over Antiochus IV, a leader of the Seleucid Empire which succeeded the Empire of Alexander the Great. Jews had lived peacefully under Seleucid rule in Israel for years until Antiochus came to power in around 200BC and persecuted all Jews who continued to practise their faith. He raided the Temple in Jerusalem and ordered an altar to the Greek god Zeus to be built inside. The Jews fought hard to protect their rights and after three years of fighting the Maccabees triumphed. The Temple was reclaimed and rededicated.

Olive oil was needed to light the menorah, a seven-branched candelabrum which was kept alight in the Temple. The Maccabees could only find enough oil to keep the eternal flame burning for one day. But miraculously, the existing oil continued to burn for not one, but eight days whilst the long task of preparing and consecrating more oil was being carried out. The word Hanukkah means dedication, as the festival marks the rededication of the Temple, and it lasts for eight days to commemorate the Miracle of the Oil. A special nine-branched menorah is used by

Jews to mark Hanukkah, with a central candle which is higher than the four candles to either side. In the evening prior to each day of the festival, prayers are said while the central candle is used to light the other candles. One is lit for the first day, two are lit for the second day, and so on. Children may be given small gifts each evening at the time the candles are lit.

Hanukkah traditions include eating foods that are fried in oil, such as potato latkes (a type of fried potato cake) and sufganiot (jam doughnut), to remember the Miracle of the Oil. Children often play games with a dreidel (a four-sided spinning top), to remind them of when Jews had to meet together to worship in secret. They would hide their Torah scrolls and pretend to be playing with a dreidel whenever any guards discovered them.

Hanukkah usually takes place in December, but occasionally falls in late November or early January.

Worksheet 1 tells the story of Hanukkah for children to read with the support of the teacher.

Worksheet 2 provides the outline of a menorah to decorate for display. Encourage pupils to notice how the central candle (shamash) is taller than the others and is used to light the appropriate number of extra candles each evening as the festival progresses. A candle flame could be added to the picture each day during the eight days of the festival.

Worksheet 3 is a matching game of words and pictures using some of the key symbols of Hanukkah. Ensure that the children understand what each item is and how it is involved in the Hanukkah celebrations.

Andrew Brodie: Festivals Across the Year 5–7 © A C Black Publishers Ltd. 2007

Hanukkah

Name .... Date ....

Jews celebrate Hanukkah to remember the Maccabees and the Miracle of the Oil.

Antiochus, the king of Israel, worshipped the Greek gods. He tried to stop the Jews from worshipping their God. He put a statue of a Greek god in the Temple of the Jews.

A group of Jews called the Maccabees decided to fight Antiochus for their freedom. After three years they defeated Antiochus and removed the statue from the Temple. The Jews didn't have enough oil to light their menorah and they needed to make some more. They only had a tiny amount of oil and it took eight days for them to fetch olives and make new oil. By a miracle, the tiny bit of oil kept the candles burning brightly for eight whole days until new oil was ready.

Hanukkah is the Jewish Festival of Light. It lasts for eight days and Jews light one candle on the menorah for each day of Hanukkah. The middle candle is lit every day.

Hanukkah

Name .... Date ....

Each evening a new candle is added to the Menorah. Carefully colour the picture.

Andrew Brodie: Festivals Across the Year 5–7 © A C Black Publishers Ltd. 2007

Hanukkah

Name .... Date ....

Cut out all the cards and match each Hanukkah picture with its name.

Temple

Dreidel

Latkes

Menorah (nine branches)

Christmas

Teacher's Notes

Background information

Christmas is when Christians celebrate the birth of Jesus Christ. Jesus was the founder of Christianity, and Christians believe that he was the Son of God.

The Christmas story is known as the Nativity. It says that an angel visited a young woman called Mary, and told her that she was going to have a baby boy who would be the Son of God and that she must call him Jesus. At the time, there was a census taking place, and Mary was required to travel with her fiancé, Joseph, to his home town of Bethlehem. They couldn't find anywhere to stay, but an inn-keeper offered them shelter in his stable, and this is where Jesus was born. Shepherds were called to the scene by angels, and wise men from the East, bringing precious gifts, followed a bright new star to the stable, after hearing a prophecy that it would lead to a new king.

Families traditionally put up a Christmas tree in their homes in the weeks leading up to Christmas. The tree is then decorated with lights, tinsel and baubles. Homes, schools, shops and offices are also often decorated. On Christmas Day, greetings cards and gifts are exchanged, and a family meal is enjoyed.

Christians go to church on Christmas morning, and some attend a service at midnight the night before, called midnight mass. Christmas carols and hymns are sung and prayers are said for peace and goodwill.

As with many religious festivals, Christmas traditions vary in different countries across the world. It takes place on 25th December.

Worksheet 1 is a missing words activity with some basic information about Christmas and how it is celebrated.

Worksheet 2 is a crib scene for pupils to colour and label. The words for the labels have been presented in such a way that less able children can cut them out and stick them into position, whilst more able pupils can write them.

Worksheet 3 provides the outline of a Christmas tree to be decorated by the children. These could then be used for display.

Christmas

Name .... Date ....

Use the words from the box to complete the information below.

At _____ Christians celebrate the birth of

_____ Christ. His mother was called _____

and his father on earth was called _____ . Mary

and Joseph travelled to _____ where

Jesus was born in a _____ . He was visited by

_____ from the fields and by

_____ men from other countries.

At Christmas people give their friends and family gifts and

_____ . Christians go to _____ where they

say prayers and sing Christmas _____

Homes are decorated with trees and coloured

_____ . On Christmas Day families

enjoy eating _____

together. This dinner will usually

include meat and vegetables and a

Christmas _____ .

Jesus
Mary
Christmas stable pudding
Joseph   shepherds
Bethlehem
church dinner
lights   carols
cards   wise

Christmas

Name ....

Date ....

Label this Christmas picture using the words at the bottom of the page. When you have finished the labels you can carefully colour the picture.

| baby | angel | wise man | Mary | Joseph | donkey | star | shepherd |

Christmas

Name .... Date ....

At Christmas, Christians decorate their houses and often have a Christmas tree.

Use colouring pencils, felt-tip pens, paper, foil, stickers or anything else you can find to colour and decorate this Christmas tree.

You can display your tree at home or in your classroom.

Chinese New Year

Teacher's Notes

Background information

Chinese New Year is the most important date in the Chinese calendar. It is also sometimes known as the Spring Festival and is considered a major holiday in China and other countries that are greatly influenced by Chinese culture, such as Mongolia, Tibet, Vietnam, Bhutan, Korea and Nepal. It is celebrated by Chinese communities across the world.

Chinese New Year is a time of parties and celebrations, of visiting friends and family to wish them good luck and prosperity in the coming year, and of much Chinese symbolism. In the days leading up to New Year, houses are thoroughly cleaned to sweep out bad luck, and just before midnight on New Year's Eve, doors and windows are left open to allow the old year to leave and the new year to enter. Brooms and mops must be put away before New Year arrives, to welcome good luck into the house and ensure that it is not swept away.

On New Year's Day, many celebrations and parades take place. Brightly coloured flags and banners are waved, and fireworks are let off to frighten away evil spirits. Big colourful dragons often take part in the parade, as dragons are a symbol of good luck, and dancers dressed as lions welcome in the new year, as lions are considered guardians.

People will leave their homes to watch the parades and to give New Year greetings to their neighbours, family and friends. New Year gifts

of money are given to younger family members in red envelopes, as red symbolises good things and is a sign of good luck. Red is widely associated with Chinese New Year, with many houses being decorated in red and children often wearing new red clothes.

The kind of food eaten at New Year is also heavily influenced by Chinese symbolism. Foods will often be eaten because their Chinese name sounds similar to common New Year greetings and wishes. Chinese dumplings are eaten because they look like gold nuggets, so they are thought of as an omen of prosperity.

The end of the New Year period is marked fifteen days later with the Lantern Festival. At this time people decorate homes and streets with lanterns and there are more fireworks and dragon parades.

Chinese New Year is based on the lunar calendar, and is usually celebrated in late January or early February.

Worksheet 1 is a missing word activity to consolidate the children's knowledge of the festival. The words can either be written in or cut out and stuck into place.

Worksheet 2 provides a template for a Chinese dragon mask. Once the children have their finished marks you could create your own New Year parade around the classroom or in an assembly. You will need to enlarge the mask depending on the size of the child's face.

Worksheet 3 is a drawing activity based on the 12 animals used to name the Chinese years.

Andrew Brodie: Festivals Across the Year 5–7 © A C Black Publishers Ltd. 2007

Chinese New Year

Name .... Date ....

Cut out the words below and stick them in the correct places in the sentences, using what you have learned about Chinese New Year.

Before the New Year celebrations begin, people clean their

_____ and put up decorations.

When it is midnight on New Year's Eve the _____

and windows are _____ to let the old year out.

Chinese New Year is a very happy time. Children are given

gifts of _____ in lucky red _____.

There are street parades with _____and

_____ dancing.

| doors | dragon | money | homes |

| fireworks | envelopes | opened |

Andrew Brodie: Festivals Across the Year 5-7 © A C Black Publishers Ltd. 2007

Chinese New Year

Name .... Date ....

The Chinese celebrate their New Year with big parades through the streets. The parades are colourful and always include people dressed up as a long Chinese dragon.

Cut out and colour the dragon mask below.

Remember to carefully cut the dotted holes out for your eyes.

You can attach a pencil to the bottom of your mask so that you can hold it up or tie some elastic to each side. Now you can have your own Chinese New Year parade!

Andrew Brodie: Festivals Across the Year 5–7 © A C Black Publishers Ltd 2007

Chinese New Year

Name .... Date ....

The Chinese years are named after the twelve different animals below. Draw a picture of each animal in the box above its name.

pig	rat	ox	tiger

rabbit	dragon	snake	horse

sheep	monkey	rooster	dog

Andrew Brodie: Festivals Across the Year 5-7 © A C Black Publishers Ltd. 2007

Holi

Teacher's Notes

Background information

Holi is celebrated by Hindus in India and all across the world. It is marked on the day after the full moon during the month of Phalunga, which usually falls in March but occasionally in late February, and it celebrates the start of spring and the new life that is associated with it. Holi is an energetic, fun-filled festival with an overwhelming spirit of good humour and goodwill.

Holi commemorates the story of Holika, sister of the demon king, who was burned to death in a fire that had been intended to kill the king's son, Prahlad (this is sometimes written Prahlada). On the evening before Holi, bonfires are lit in the streets in India, and coconuts are roasted in the flames to remember the story. In some parts of India, a model of Holika is thrown onto the bonfire. The message of the story is of good winning over evil and of the god Vishnu's protection of those who are faithful to him.

While the origins of Holi are rooted in religious stories, there are no major religious rituals which should be performed during the festival. Holi is also known as the Festival of Colour, as people throw brightly coloured powders or coloured water at each other and at passers by, shouting 'Don't feel offended, it's

Holi!' It is a very messy affair as people are drenched in colour, and the air is filled with all the coloured powder. The feeling of goodwill at Holi is reinforced as differences of caste, wealth, gender and age are put aside. Everyone is so covered in colour that it is difficult to tell who is rich and who is poor!

Holi is also a time of singing and dancing, and in the evening friends and families eat big celebratory meals together to round off the festivities.

Practical Activity

This activity can be great fun on a warm day but you should ask parents' permission first. You will obviously need to take account of Health and Safety issues. Have buckets of water each coloured a different colour with a little food colouring. Invite pupils to bring a change of clothes (old shorts and t-shirt are ideal), a towel and a water pistol. Mark out an area of the playground in which the children can soak each other, leaving those outside the area clean and dry, and recreate Holi by squirting the coloured water at each other. It is better if at least one member of staff joins in to help reinforce the notion that children are allowed to throw their powders or coloured water at adults during Holi.

Worksheet 1 provides the children with sentences about Holi activities to illustrate.

Worksheet 2 reinforces the children's knowledge of Holi and its customs with a missing word activity. The words can be written in or cut out and stuck into place.

Worksheet 3 provides the outline of a Holi bonfire for the children to decorate and display.

Andrew Brodie: Festivals Across the Year 5–7 © A C Black Publishers Ltd. 2007

Holi

Name .... Date ....

In spring the festival of Holi is enjoyed by many Hindu people.

Draw a picture for each sentence.

> 1

People sing and dance around large bonfires.

> 2

Brightly coloured powders and water are thrown over people.

 # Holi

Name .... Date ....

These sentences are about Holi. Use what you have learned to fill the gap in each sentence with the correct word at the bottom of this sheet.

1 Holi is a festival celebrated by _____ .

2 At Holi, Hindus remember how the god _____

saved Prince Prahlad from his evil father.

3 Hindus light _____ and sometimes throw

dummies of Holika onto the flames.

4 Holi is also known as the Festival of _____ .

5 Children run through the streets throwing coloured

_____ at passers-by.

6 As they throw the powder they shout "Don't feel

offended, it's _____ !"

bonfires   Hindus   Colour

powder   Holi   Vishnu

Andrew Brodie: Festivals Across the Year 5–7 © A C Black Publishers Ltd. 2007

Holi

Name .... Date ....

Decorate the flames and use them to make a picture of a Holi bonfire. Remember that Holi is the 'Festival of Colour', so make your bonfire as colourful as you can!

Pesach

Teacher's Notes

Pesach, or Passover, is the most anticipated festival in the Jewish calendar and is celebrated by Jews everywhere. It takes place in March or April and it lasts for seven days in Israel and eight days elsewhere.

Pesach celebrates the exodus of the Israelites from slavery in ancient Egypt, under the leadership of Moses. Jews believe that God sent Moses to ask Pharaoh to release the Israelites from Egypt, but Pharaoh refused. God then gave Moses the power to release a series of plagues, which killed many Egyptians and all Egyptian livestock. Before inflicting the tenth and final plague, God told the Israelites to slaughter a lamb and smear its blood on their door frames. They were then to roast the lamb and eat it with bitter herbs, and be ready for a long journey. Jews commemorate this meal at Pesach.

The final plague was the death of every firstborn son in Egypt, but the plague 'passed over' all the houses which had lamb's blood smeared on the door frame. This is where the name 'Passover' comes from. Once this plague had hit, the Egyptians pleaded with Pharaoh to banish the Israelites from Egypt. He agreed and the Israelites fled, taking their bread with them which had not had time to rise. While fleeing through the desert they ate this unleavened bread, and for this reason only unleavened bread is allowed during the festival of Pesach.

Any foods that contain yeast as a rising agent are not permitted for the duration of the festival, and Jewish houses must be thoroughly cleaned and cleared out before Pesach to ensure that none of these foods, or anything that has been used to prepare them are in the house. Special sets of crockery and cutlery are reserved for use on Passover only.

The Pesach meal, or the Seder, includes many practices which must all be carried out in a specific order and carry much symbolism from the Pesach story. The meal can take several hours to complete. The Seder plate is a specially decorated plate for the following items:

A roasted shankbone (A reminder of the lamb sacrificed on the night of the Passover)

Bitter herbs (To represent the bitterness of slavery)

An egg (A reminder of the cycle of life)

Haroset (A paste made from apples, walnuts, cinnamon and wine that represents the mortar used by the Israelite slaves in Egypt)

Karpas (A green vegetable to dip in salt water to represent the tears of the slaves)

Worksheet 1 provides information about Pesach suitable for guided reading or as a focus for discussion in assembly. Use these Teacher's Notes and the book of Exodus in the Bible to supplement this information.

Worksheet 2 provides the children with two Pesach-related images and asks them to describe what they are, and their importance to the festival.

Worksheet 3 is a Pesach wordsearch to reinforce the vocabulary of this festival.

Andrew Brodie: Festivals Across the Year 5–7 © A C Black Publishers Ltd. 2007

Pesach

Name .... Date ....

Read the information on this page.

Every year Jews celebrate the Pesach festival. This is when they remember that many years ago God helped them to escape from the Ancient Egyptians. They needed to escape as they were used as slaves and had to work hard in the hot sun helping to build the pyramids.

Before Pesach, Jewish people make sure their houses are very clean. They throw away some foods that they are not allowed to eat during the week long festival. They may get out special sets of plates, bowls, knives, forks and spoons that they only use during Pesach.

There is a special family meal held as part of the celebration of Pesach. At this meal there are things that have to be said and done. Questions are asked by the youngest member of the family, and these are answered by the head of the family. The questions and answers are all about why the festival is celebrated and what is believed to have happened all those years ago.

A very important part of the meal is the 'Seder Plate'. This is a large plate with some foods on it that help Jews to think about the Pesach festival. There are also special biscuits called matzos that are eaten instead of bread.

Andrew Brodie: Festivals Across the Year 5-7 © A C Black Publishers Ltd. 2007

 # Pesach

Name .... Date ....

In your own words, describe the pictures, and why they are important to the Pesach festival. When you have finished you can carefully colour the pictures.

....
....
....

....
....
....

....
....
....

....
....

Andrew Brodie: Festivals Across the Year 5–7 © A C Black Publishers Ltd. 2007

Pesach

Name .... Date ....

Look for the words in the word search. They might be written forwards or backwards, up or down.

| frogs | hail | Seder plate |

| family meal | Pesach | escape | locusts |

S	L	A	V	E	S	E	E	D	F
E	Q	L	M	G	T	A	C	R	A
D	G	O	D	Y	A	A	L	B	M
E	N	D	A	P	L	C	E	O	I
R	G	N	A	T	S	H	A	I	L
P	E	S	A	C	H	G	N	L	Y
L	O	C	U	S	T	S	H	S	M
A	F	L	I	E	S	O	O	F	E
T	L	F	R	O	G	S	M	Z	A
E	S	C	A	P	E	X	E	T	L

| clean home | flies | gnats | God |

| boils | slaves | Egypt |

Andrew Brodie: Festivals Across the Year 5–7 © A C Black Publishers Ltd. 2007

Easter

Teacher's Notes

Easter is the most important Christian festival as it celebrates the resurrection of Jesus Christ from the dead, the event which forms the basis of Christianity itself. It is celebrated by all Christians in March or early April each year.

In the weeks before Easter, Christians remember the events leading up to the death and resurrection of Jesus. Lent is the period of forty days (excluding Sundays) before Easter; it is traditionally a time of prayer and fasting before the celebrations on Easter Day. Nowadays, Christians often give up something they enjoy for these forty days, instead of fasting.

Palm Sunday is the Sunday before Easter, on which Christians remember when Jesus rode into Jerusalem on a donkey to the adulation of the crowds who made a carpet of palm leaves in front of him. They also think about Christ and his disciples eating the Last Supper together as Jesus foretold his betrayal by Judas to the Roman guards and his execution for blasphemy.

The main focus of the festival is on the Easter weekend. Good Friday is a time of reflection and prayer as Christians remember when Jesus was crucified by the Romans. They believe that Jesus died to take the blame for the sins of all Christians, but that he rose from the dead on the Sunday and appeared to some of his disciples. This is what Christians celebrate on Easter Sunday.

Easter is a spring festival and as such has connections with new life. For this reason, chocolate eggs are often given to children on Easter Sunday.

Worksheet 1 provides an Easter card for the children to decorate.

Worksheet 2 invites the children to make an Easter box. The pictures on the box provide stimulus for discussion.

Worksheet 3 provides the outline of an egg to decorate along with some explanation as to why eggs are given at Easter.

Andrew Brodie: Festivals Across the Year 5–7 © A C Black Publishers Ltd. 2007

Easter

Name .... Date ....

Colour the picture carefully.
Cut along the bold line, fold along the dotted line
and your picture will stand up.

Easter

Name .... Date ....

Easter Box

Colour the pictures. Cut along the bold lines. Fold along the dotted lines. Put glue on the tabs. Carefully stick your box together.

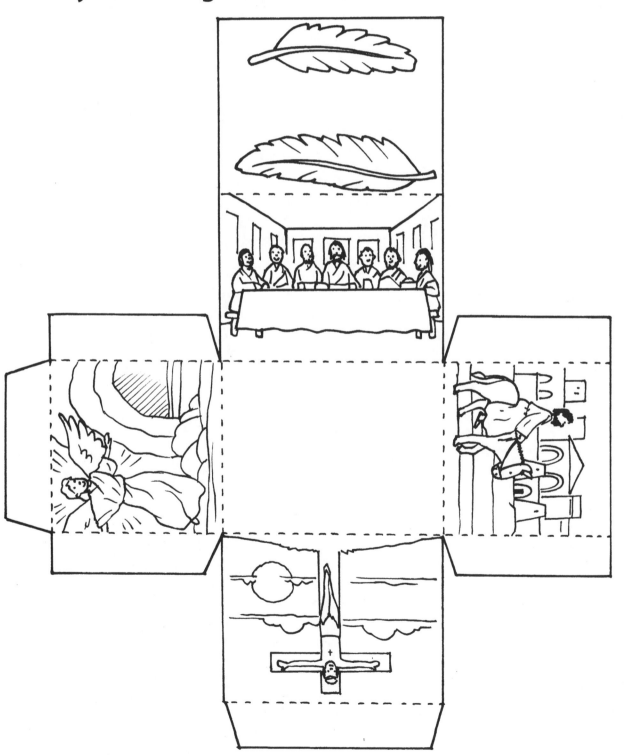

Andrew Brodie: Festivals Across the Year 5–7 © A C Black Publishers Ltd. 2007

Easter

Name .... Date ....

Easter Egg Puzzle

✩ **At Easter time we think of the signs of springtime around us. Look carefully at the egg and you will find some spring life.**

Colour the
chicken
brown.

Colour the
rabbit black.
Colour the
chick yellow.

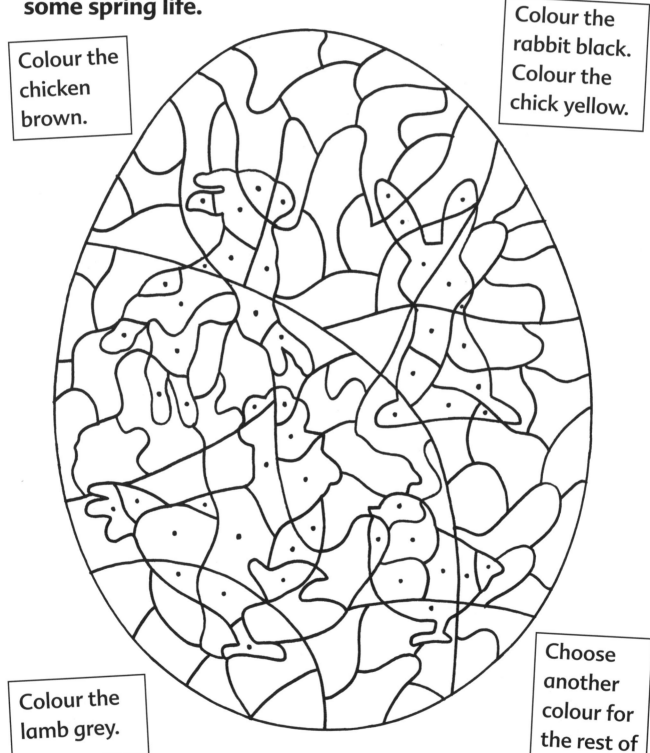

Colour the
lamb grey.

Choose
another
colour for
the rest of
the egg.

Baisakhi

Teacher's Notes

Background information

Baisakhi is a religious festival which celebrates the beginning of the Sikh religion as it is known today.

Long before Baisakhi took on new significance for the Sikh faith it had been celebrated as the Punjabi New Year and the first day of the harvest in the Punjab region of India. Crowds would gather at Keshgarh Sahib near Anandpur to mark the beginning of the year, to hope for a good harvest season, and to listen to the guru.

Guru Teg Bahadur was the ninth Sikh guru. In 1657, the Mughal Emperor, Aurangzeb, declared himself the Emperor of India and tried to make all of India Muslim. He persecuted Hindus and Sikhs, so Guru Teg Bahadur made his young son, Gobind Rai, the tenth guru and went to Delhi to try end the suffering of the Hindus and Sikhs. Guru Teg Bahadur was seized by Aurangzeb and executed. His body was left in a heap after the execution, but not a single Sikh was brave enough to step forward and claim the body so that religious rites could be performed on it for fear that he too would be killed.

Guru Gobind Rai was angered by this and in 1699 he called for Sikhs from far and wide to

make a special effort to attend the Baisakhi celebrations at Keshgarh Sahib. He wanted to raise the spirits of the downtrodden Sikhs and give them a strong identity in the face of this persecution, and did this by initiating the community of Khalsa. Hundreds of thousands of people gathered as the guru made a long and emotive speech about the need for a spirit of courage and sacrifice, like that of his father. This sets the scene for the story of Baisakhi told on Worksheet 1.

On the day of Baisakhi, Sikhs gather early at their Gurdwaras for a special prayer meeting. Five Sikhs who represent the Five Beloved Ones of the Baisakhi story read the same verses that were read in 1699. Everyone is given amrit to sip and devotes themselves to the community of Khalsa. Religious songs are sung before everyone takes part in a community lunch known as guru-ka-langar. Later in the day, the Sikh holy book which is also thought of as the final guru, the Guru Granth Sahib, is processed through the streets as people chant and sing.

In the Punjab region of India, Baisakhi is also still remembered as a harvest festival and is often celebrated with traditional bhangra and gidda dancing. Baisakhi usually falls on 13th April, but once every 36 years it falls on 14th April.

Worksheet 1 gives a simple account of the Baisakhi story and introduces the Five Ks.

Worksheet 2 shows a traditionally dressed Sikh. The Five Ks should be labelled.

Worksheet 3 is a matching activity of words and pictures about Baisakhi customs and traditions.

Baisakhi

Read about the festival of Baisakhi.

The festival of Baisakhi is held on 13th April each year. It celebrates the new year, the growing of crops and the harvest. Special dancing called 'Bhangra' is often seen at this festival. 'Bhangra' is dancing that tells the story of the harvest from the seeds being sown to the crops being gathered in. It is very cheerful dancing, drummers play exciting rhythms and the dancers wear bright costumes.

Baisakhi is also the day when all people who wish to follow the Sikh faith take part in the ceremony of 'Amrit'. Amrit is a drink made in a special way from sugar and water. People who wish to take part in this ceremony must be wearing the five K's of the Sikh religion. The five K's are: Kes (hair that is not cut), Kanga, (a comb), Kirpan (a sword with a curved blade), Kara (a bangle worn on the wrist of the right hand) and Kachh (a pair of cotton shorts).

Baisakhi is a very happy day and after meeting and praying in the Gurdwara the Sikh people will all eat a meal together.

Draw a picture about the festival of Baisakhi on a separate sheet of paper.

Andrew Brodie: Festivals Across the Year 5-7 © A C Black Publishers Ltd. 2007

Baisakhi

Name .... Date ....

Label each item on the picture.

Andrew Brodie: Festivals Across the Year 5–7 © A C Black Publishers Ltd. 2007

Baisakhi

Name .... Date ....

Match the writing to the pictures.

_____

_____

_____

_____

_____

_____

_____

_____

_____

_____

Verses about Baisakhi are read out loud.	People drink amrit which is made of sugar and water.
Outside the Gurdwara the Sikh flag flies.	After the service in the Gurdwara everyone eats together.

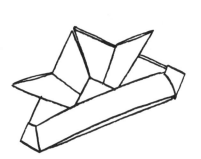

Children's Day

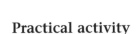

Teacher's Notes

Background information

Kodomo No Hi, or Children's Day, is celebrated in Japan on 5th May each year. It is a day when families celebrate the health, growth and happiness of their children.

This festival is thought to have originated from an ancient Chinese festival and became popular in Japan about fifteen hundred years ago. It is a national holiday and was originally known as Boys' Day. The Japanese also celebrate Hina Matsuri, or Girls' Day, annually on 3rd March but it is not marked as a national holiday, so, due to some feeling that this was unfair, Boys' Day was adapted in 1948 to include both sexes and is now thought of as Children's Day. Despite this, the customs and traditions of Children's Day are still mainly associated with boys.

In Samurai times, armour and helmets were decorated to strengthen the spirit of young boys who were trained and ready to fight from around the age of 15. Today, dolls of famous warriors are displayed in homes and shops on Children's Day, and other customs mainly symbolise strength and success. The koi carp is the symbol of Children's Day as it represents energy, courage and spirit – once thought of as qualities needed for boy warriors, but now recognised as desirable features in all healthy, growing children.

As well as Children's Day and Girls' Day, the Japanese also celebrate a festival called Shichi-Go-San, which means Seven-Five-Three. On this day they celebrate any children aged 7, 5 or 3 as they believe that these are the ages at which children grow the most.

Practical activity

Children could investigate koi carp, their colourings and their characteristics. Use this information to help pupils better understand why the characteristics of the carp make them a suitable symbol for Children's Day.

Worksheet 1 gives some simple text with comprehension questions about the customs of Children's Day.

Worksheet 2 provides a chart to complete concerning what pupils feel make their parents proud of them, and what their parents do for them. This can easily be incorporated into P.S.H.E work and would make an effective focus for an assembly.

Worksheet 3 gives the outline of a koi carp shape to be filled in with collage to form a Children's Day display. This is most effective if the carps are photocopied in a variety of different sizes.

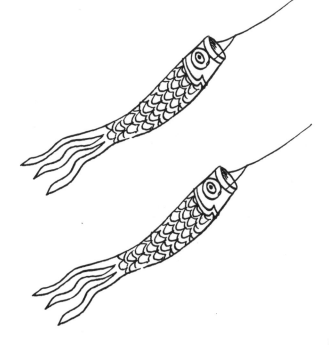

Andrew Brodie: Festivals Across the Year 5–7 © A C Black Publishers Ltd 2007

Children's Day

Name .... Date ....

Children's Day is celebrated in Japan every year in May. On this day parents are thankful that their children are healthy and growing strongly. Children are thankful for the care and love given to them by their parents. On Children's Day flags shaped like fish are flown outside family homes. The fish are brightly coloured koi carp. There is one for each child, flying from bamboo flagpoles.

Read the questions and put a ring around the correct answer.

Children's Day in Japan is celebrated in which month?

March   April   May   June

What are children thankful to their parents for?

Fruit and vegetables   Love and care   Health and growth

What shape are flags flown outside homes?

Flowers   Fish   Frogs   Flies

What are the flagpoles made from?

Bangers   Boots   Bamboo   Boys

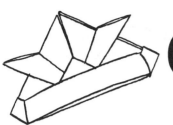

Children's Day

Name .... Date ....

Children's Day is a day for parents to be thankful for the good things about their children. Children are also thankful for everything their parents do for them.

Draw or write about three things about yourself that you are proud of. These may be things you are good at, or anything that you like about yourself.

Draw or write about three things you would like to thank your parents for.

Andrew Brodie: Festivals Across the Year 5–7 © A C Black Publishers Ltd. 2007

Children's Day

Name ....

Date ....

Use the template to cut out scales of brightly coloured foil or paper to cover this koi carp.

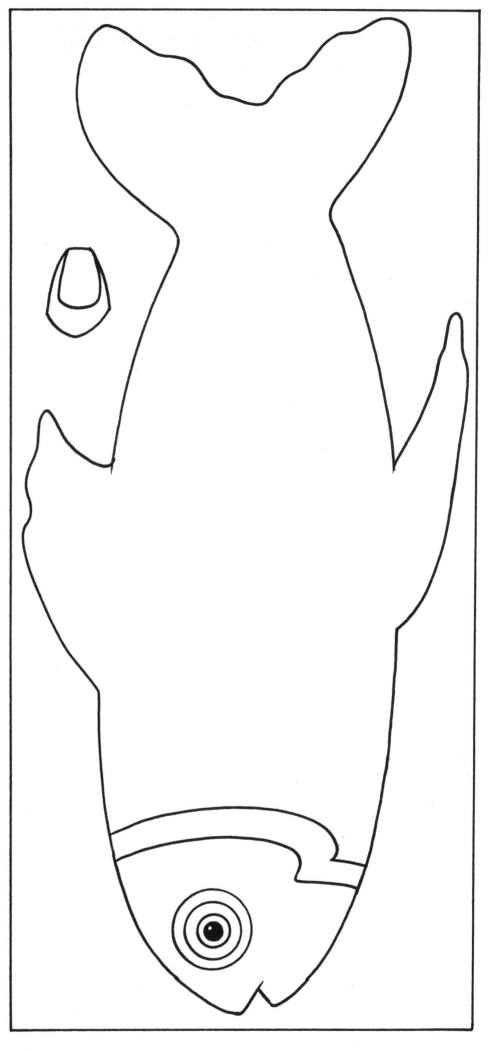

Wesak

Teacher's Notes

Background information

The festival of Wesak (sometimes spelt Vesak) is the most important in the Buddhist calendar and is celebrated by Buddhists all over the world. Wesak takes place on the day of the full moon in May, or very occasionally in early June. It celebrates the birth, 'Enlightenment' and death of Siddhartha Gautama, who became known as the Buddha, which means 'Enlightened one'.

Wesak is a very joyful festival, but is generally marked with a day of reflection and holiness, rather than more common festivities such as music and dancing. The Buddha was a holy man who wanted to end suffering and sought happiness and inner peace by rejecting worldly possessions and pleasures. Wesak is a day for all Buddhists to remember the story of the Buddha's enlightenment by living and promoting the core values of Buddhism which were taught by the Buddha. It is also a time to bring happiness to less fortunate people and money is often donated to charities with this in mind. In Buddhist countries, shops which sell alcohol will often be closed down for two days over Wesak as Buddhists should abstain from alcohol and all other intoxicating substances. Even food is thought of as a human indulgence, and must be eaten in moderation. Any food eaten at Wesak is usually vegetarian, as the Buddha taught that animals should not be harmed.

Buddhists will often clean their houses in preparation for the festival and might help to decorate their local temple with paintings or lights. Buddhists will go to the temple early on the morning of Wesak to meditate and to reaffirm their faith. They may bring small offerings of candles, joss-sticks or flowers (lotus) for the monks to remind them of how all life must eventually come to an end, like that of a flower or candle. It is important to understand that the Buddha is not worshipped as a god, but is thought of as a guide whose teachings should be followed by Buddhists worldwide. He is an inspiration for all Buddhists who seek to achieve 'Enlightenment', a state of mind which transcends suffering and human desire.

Buddhism is followed by people from countries in all parts of the world and its customs have often been influenced by the different cultures that have embraced them. As a result, Wesak celebrations vary from country to country. In China, dragon dancing is sometimes part of the Wesak celebrations and in Indonesia and Sri Lanka decorative lanterns are a feature of the festival.

Worksheet 1 provides background information for pupils to read which can be used for guided reading.

Worksheet 2 asks children to complete a dot to dot to show the symbolic lotus flower.

Worksheet 3 is a matching pictures and sentences activity about Wesak customs.

Andrew Brodie: Festivals Across the Year 5-7 © A C Black Publishers Ltd 2007

Wesak

Name .... Date ....

Read about the festival of Wesak and draw a picture in the box below.

Each year Buddhists enjoy the festival of Wesak. This is the time when the life of the Buddha is celebrated. It is the most important festival of the year.

Wesak usually takes place on the day of the full moon in May. Houses are cleaned and decorations are put up. These decorations are often colourful lights and flowers.

Going to the temple is an important part of the festival. In some countries water is poured over statues of the Buddha; this is called bathing the Buddha.

In some parts of the world lots of lanterns are used to light the streets. There can be processions and firework displays as part of the celebrations. In China there is sometimes dragon dancing at Wesak.

It is important to think of others during Wesak and cards are given to friends.

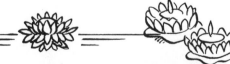

 # Wesak

Name .... Date ....

In Buddhism lotus flowers are a sign of purity. Buddhist temples are often decorated with lotus flowers at Wesak.

Join the dots to make a lotus flower.
Then colour in or decorate your flower.

Andrew Brodie: Festivals Across the Year 5–7 © A C Black Publishers Ltd 2007

Wesak

Name .... Date ....

Find the correct sentence for each picture. Copy or stick the sentences below the pictures.

Buddhists celebrate Wesak because it is the Buddha's birthday.	It is a holy day and people take flowers and candles to the temple.
Houses are cleaned the night before Wesak.	Money is given to charities to help less fortunate people.

Resource Sheet A: Cycle of festivals

The wheels below show the order in which some of the main festivals occur in each major religion and in the Chinese culture. Each wheel shows more festivals than those featured in this book. This enables the information to be used when studying a particular religion. The exact dates of many of these festivals vary from year to year.

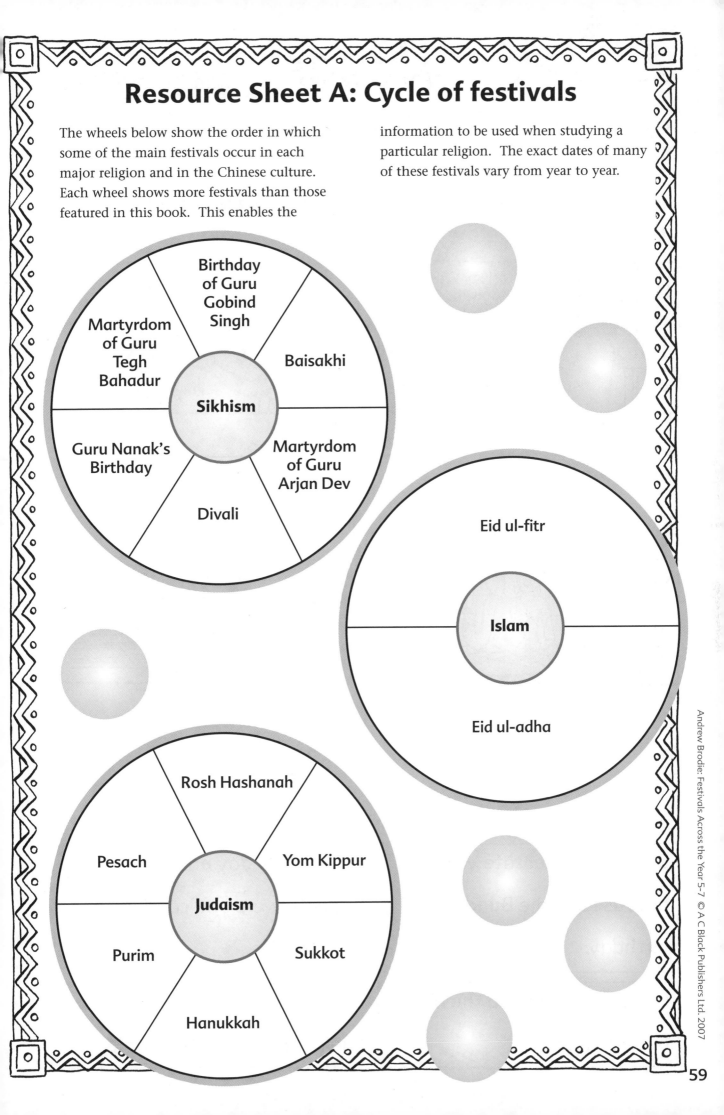

Sikhism
- Birthday of Guru Gobind Singh
- Baisakhi
- Martyrdom of Guru Arjan Dev
- Divali
- Guru Nanak's Birthday
- Martyrdom of Guru Tegh Bahadur

Islam
- Eid ul-fitr
- Eid ul-adha

Judaism
- Rosh Hashanah
- Yom Kippur
- Sukkot
- Hanukkah
- Purim
- Pesach

Andrew Brodie: Festivals Across the Year 5–7 © A C Black Publishers Ltd. 2007

Resource Sheet B: Cycle of festivals

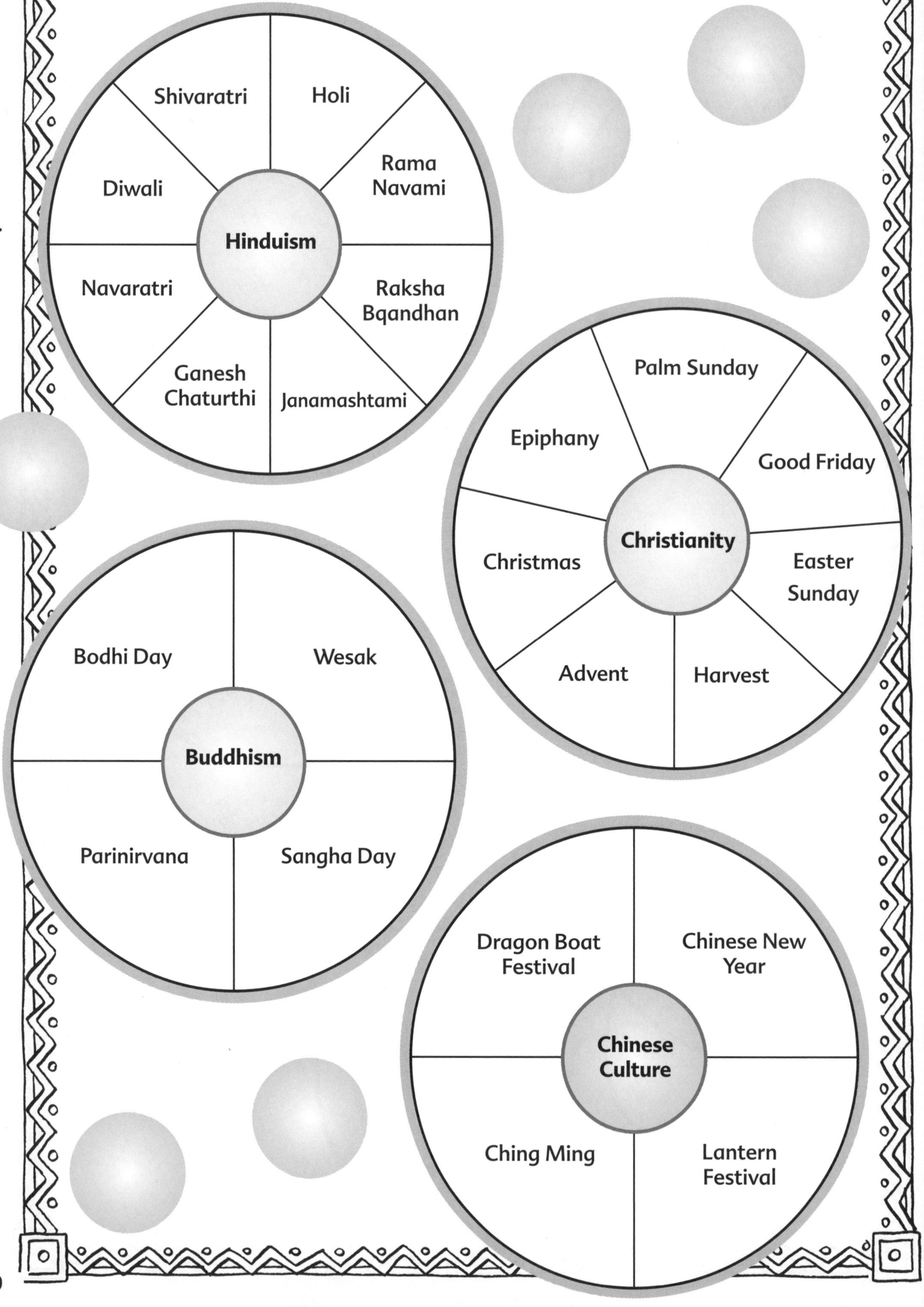

Hinduism

- Shivaratri
- Holi
- Rama Navami
- Diwali
- Navaratri
- Raksha Bqandhan
- Ganesh Chaturthi
- Janamashtami

Christianity

- Palm Sunday
- Epiphany
- Good Friday
- Christmas
- Easter Sunday
- Advent
- Harvest

Buddhism

- Bodhi Day
- Wesak
- Parinirvana
- Sangha Day

Chinese Culture

- Dragon Boat Festival
- Chinese New Year
- Ching Ming
- Lantern Festival

Resource Sheet C

Sikhism

Islam

Hinduism

Andrew Brodie: Festivals Across the Year 5–7 © A C Black Publishers Ltd. 2007

Resource Sheet D

Buddhism

Christianity

Judaism

Andrew Brodie: Festivals Across the Year 5-7 © A C Black Publishers Ltd. 2007

Resource Sheet E

Andrew Brodie: Festivals Across the Year 5–7 © A C Black Publishers Ltd. 2007

Resource Sheet F

Find the words in the word search.

Some are written from left to right ➡️
and some are written from top to bottom. ⬇️

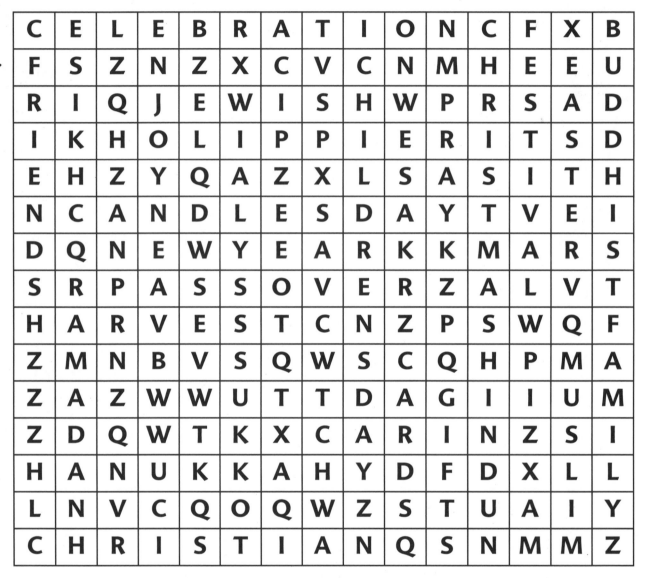

C	E	L	E	B	R	A	T	I	O	N	C	F	X	B
F	S	Z	N	Z	X	C	V	C	N	M	H	E	E	U
R	I	Q	J	E	W	I	S	H	W	P	R	S	A	D
I	K	H	O	L	I	P	P	I	E	R	I	T	S	D
E	H	Z	Y	Q	A	Z	X	L	S	A	S	I	T	H
N	C	A	N	D	L	E	S	D	A	Y	T	V	E	I
D	Q	N	E	W	Y	E	A	R	K	K	M	A	R	S
S	R	P	A	S	S	O	V	E	R	Z	A	L	V	T
H	A	R	V	E	S	T	C	N	Z	P	S	W	Q	F
Z	M	N	B	V	S	Q	W	S	C	Q	H	P	M	A
Z	A	Z	W	W	U	T	T	D	A	G	I	I	U	M
Z	D	Q	W	T	K	X	C	A	R	I	N	Z	S	I
H	A	N	U	K	K	A	H	Y	D	F	D	X	L	L
L	N	V	C	Q	O	Q	W	Z	S	T	U	A	I	Y
C	H	R	I	S	T	I	A	N	Q	S	N	M	M	Z

Jewish   Sikh   Muslim   Hindu   Buddhist   candles

celebration   festival   enjoy   Holi   family

Hanukkah   Easter   Christmas   Christian   harvest

New Year   friends   Passover   Wesak   Ramadan

Sukkot   children's day   cards   gifts   pray

Andrew Brodie: Festivals Across the Year 5-7 © A C Black Publishers Ltd. 2007